NAT LOVE
Negro Cowboy

OTHER BOOKS BY HAROLD W. FELTON

Legends of Paul Bunyan
Pecos Bill: Texas Cowpuncher
John Henry and His Hammer
Fire-Fightin' Mose
Bowleg Bill: Seagoing Cowpuncher
Cowboy Jamboree: Western Songs and Lore
New Tall Tales of Pecos Bill
Mike Fink: Best of the Keelboatmen
A Horse Named Justin Morgan
Sergeant O'Keefe and His Mule, Balaam
William Phips and the Treasure Ship
Pecos Bill and the Mustang
Jim Beckwourth, Negro Mountain Man
Edward Rose, Negro Trail Blazer
True Tall Tales of Stormalong

NAT LOVE
Negro Cowboy

HAROLD W. FELTON
Illustrated by David Hodges

Dodd, Mead & Company, New York

For Lillian and Ernie

Contents

Introduction

NAT LOVE WAS BORN a slave in 1854. He died in Los Angeles in 1921 at the age of sixty-seven. While he had no early formal schooling he learned to read and write well enough to turn out an account of his life. His autobiography was published in 1907. He had something he wanted to say. The message was that he had lived an exciting and a happy life and was proud of it.

In later years his work as a pullman porter and then as a bank guard gave him great satisfaction. He felt the same gratification in his early life as a cowboy, but there his joy was compounded because of the excitement, adventure, derring-do, and the contest with the raw, harsh nature of his environment.

Nat was not bothered by false modesty. But there was no cause to be, for a cowboy's life was filled with adventure and excitement and danger. In his book he declared that he was "nerveless," "cool," and felt he "could defy the world." This sense of power was based on a firm foundation, for it rested on his considerable ability with horses, shooting irons, and a long rope. He possessed superior skill in the use of the tools of his trade, and knew it. In entering a target shooting contest, he had no doubt about his sure success. "If a man can hit a running buffalo at 200 yards, he can hit pretty much of anything he shoots at."

Nat Love lived in a rough, cowboy world. His life was brushed with the tall-tale mystique. He wonders at the dangers he experienced: "One moment we are rejoicing that we are alive; the next we are so near the jaws of death that it seems it would be almost a miracle that our lives be saved."

I have related here some of his earlier adventures of the days of his youth and on the western cattle ranges. I have not felt obliged to follow Nat's book in every detail as much as I have tried to use the material to tell of the adventures of a cowboy who enjoyed it all so much and who, with good reason, was proud enough of it to put it down in writing and give it to others.

Nat's life was that of one of the millions whose lives are the fabric of society. The fabric is smooth, the design is pleasing, it covers and warms, it looks well and wears well when it is made of people of Nat Love's qualities. Lives such as his teach us much, perhaps more, than those of "leaders" who ordinarily write autobiographies. In them it is plain to see the reasons for the advance of the nation and of the world. The "leaders," though they may be talented and capable, succeed and become great because the people back of them have succeeded and become great in their own way. Nat Love was one of those people.

HAROLD W. FELTON

1

Black Highwayman

NAT LOVE LOOKED AT THE HORSE in the barnyard. The animal's dark mane waved like a black flag as he shook his head. "He's blacker than I am," Nat said with a grin. "And he's got a name that fits him like a glove—Black Highwayman!"

"He sure is a black horse and that's the truth," said Bill Williams. Bill was several years older than Nat, but he couldn't ride the wild, unbroken horses the way the younger boy could. Bill's father was only too glad to pay Nat for a job Nat would have been willing to do for nothing. Nat liked horses and was delighted to have the chance to ride them.

"You've been breaking all our horses to ride for ten cents apiece," Bill pointed out. "I don't see why ten cents ain't enough for Black Highwayman too."

"I already told you he's five times wilder than any other horse you got," said Nat.

"Maybe he is, but fifty cents is too much money," Bill replied.

Nat turned to his companion. "We agreed he's five times meaner than the others, so I ought to get fifty cents to break him. If he's five times meaner, I ought to get five times more money."

Bill Williams answered with a strong argument. "But I ain't got fifty cents. You broke ten horses to ride yesterday and you earned a dollar. That's pretty good money."

"Yeah," said Nat. "A dollar. Breaking your father's horses to ride is better than working for Mr. Brooks. I worked for him for a dollar and fifty cents a month and it wasn't 'til two months later that I got three dollars a month. But we got to figure how hard a job is and who is able to do it. Anyone can chop cotton or pick worms off of tobacco plants, but everyone can't break horses to ride, and Black Highwayman—"

"All I got is a quarter," said Bill.

"I sure can't argue with that," said Nat. "If that's all you've got, I'll break him for a quarter. Let's get him in the barn so's I can get on him."

Nat Love, fifteen years old, had been born in a log cabin in Davidson County, Tennessee, on a June day in 1854. He didn't know which day because no one kept a record of the day slaves were born.

Nat, with his father and mother and his sister and brother, had been the slaves of Robert Love until freedom came at the close of the Civil War. His sister Sally was eight years old and his brother Jordan was five when Nat was born.

Robert Love had been a kind man and, as slave owners went, a good master. Nat's father, Sampson, was respected by his owner and had acted as foreman of the field hands. Nat's mother was the cook in Mr. Love's kitchen, with added duties of milking cows, running a loom, weaving and making clothing for the other slaves, and helping in the vegetable garden. The children helped their parents and were given chores to do.

When Nat was seven years old, Robert Love had joined General Lee's forces and took Nat's father with him to help build forts and to work with the Confederate Army.

Everyone, slaves and slave owners, talked about the war. Among Nat's friends there was no doubt about which side was right, and the children's games showed it. Every one of them wanted to be a Yankee and no one wanted to be a Rebel.

Nat organized a "Yankee Regiment" and led it in search of an enemy. The small, rag-tail band was not long in finding one. It was a nest of yellow jackets. The boys cried with joy that a suitable foe had been discovered. No one liked yellow jackets and it was an army that could fight back.

After Nat's wounded "soldiers" recovered from their stings

they went on other raids in the fields and woods. They had
another battle with a company of bumblebees, and a lively
skirmish with hornets. But it was a nest of wasps that gave the
youthful regiment its hardest fight. The boys retreated, re-
formed, and charged again. Their weapons were old brooms
and at the end, when the last enemy wasp fell, almost every
soldier was wounded. Nat had been stung on the nose and it
swelled so much he had trouble seeing for a few days.

When the Union Army passed through the neighborhood,
it stripped the plantations clean of provisions and farm produce,
and the Negro slaves suffered much misery and hardship.

After General Lee's Army surrendered, Nat's father and his
master came home. Nat's father rented twenty acres of land
and began to work for himself. Times were bad. Sampson Love,
with the help of Nat and Jordan, made brooms, mats, and chair
bottoms from straw, cane, and reeds. He carried a large load a
dozen miles to town. When he was able to sell his goods he
came home with seed for spring planting and simple food to
vary the diet of ash cake, bran, and cracklings. The hard years
of the Civil War were followed by years of poverty as the
family struggled for existence on a small, scrubby farm.

Nat's father died when the boy was fourteen and his married
sister died shortly after. Her two small children were brought
to the home Nat shared with his mother, and they looked to
him and his brother, Jordan, for support. Jordan was not able
to give much help as he was having a hard time supporting his
own growing family.

Nat had never been to school, but his father had been taught to read and write and do sums, and the boy learned these skills from his father. He was quick-witted and soon was managing figures and words better than his teacher.

The little family made a scant living, working the poor land, and added to it by gathering wild berries and nuts, making baskets to sell, and doing odd jobs.

And here Nat was, doing a very odd job, breaking horses to ride, bareback, at ten cents each.

Black Highwayman was not an ordinary horse. He was bigger than the others and, as Nat had said, five times wilder.

"Here's your twenty-five cents," said Bill.

Nat took the coin and spat on it lightly. "That's for luck," he said. He rubbed it on his torn sleeve and then tied it in the corner of his shirttail. "Now lead me to that horse."

The two boys drove the wild creature into the barn and locked the door. Nat would approach this horse as he had the others. He would mount with a leap from a partition between the stalls. At that moment Bill would open the barn door and the horse would dash into the barnyard, trying in every fashion known to horses to free himself of the rider. Nat, for his part, would try in every way known to him to stay on the bucking animal's back.

The boy had one advantage. He had ridden horses before, wild untamed ones. He had experience and the skill that comes from it. The horses, on the other hand, had never been ridden though they all pitched and ran and bucked like professionals. Then, too, they weighed up to half a ton while Nat tipped the scales at less than a hundred pounds.

It took courage to get up on the backs of the wild horses, and it took skill to stay there, but these were qualities Nat Love had in good supply. To tell the truth, he rode the horses for the fun of it as much as for the money. He always figured there was nothing wrong in liking the job you had.

Black Highwayman was not easy to fork, but Nat finally did it with a flying leap from the stall partition. The black horse didn't like the idea the least bit and in the first few seconds he crashed several times against the stalls. Nat's feet and legs would have been crushed if he had not seen each impact coming and raised his legs.

"Open the door!" he yelled. "Open it!"

Bill was struggling with the latch. The door swung open. Black Highwayman shot out of the barn like a cannon ball and uncorked himself. He wrinkled his spine and raged in a bucking frenzy around the small barnyard.

There was not enough space for the big black horse. He made a dash for the fence and flew over it like a black cloud. Mr. Williams' hounds, barking as though they were on the scent of a bear, followed horse and rider over the fields. Black Highwayman cleared the fences, ditches, and hedges as though they weren't there, while Nat stuck to his back like a leech.

It wasn't the most comfortable place he could think of, but

then he had not started out in search of comfort. Besides, he thought, quite sensibly, there was no good opportunity to get off, although Black Highwayman was trying his level best to bring that about.

The horse ran several miles and then began to circle back. By this time every dog in the neighborhood had joined the chase and the neighbors had mounted horses and started in wild pursuit. In every pasture the pell-mell group dashed through, a small stampede of horses and cows was created.

"I'm going to break this critter or break my neck," Nat muttered grimly as he clung to his mount.

Suddenly, when it seemed as though the mad race had no end, Black Highwayman stopped. He was exhausted and knew that he was a beaten horse. He had not been able to throw the boy from his back.

The neighbors caught up. "That was some ridin'," said one.

"Best ridin' I ever seen," said another.

"Why, it ain't no one but that kid Nat Love," another exclaimed, surprised that a young boy could have ridden Black Highwayman to a standstill.

"What do you mean, kid? He rides like a man. Better than most men. That was the best ridin' ever."

The praise warmed Nat. It felt good—like sitting in the warm sun on the south side of a haystack on a cool April day.

But there was something else that was important too. That was his pay for riding the big black horse. The twenty-five cents. Confidently he reached down for the quarter he had tied in his shirttail, a shirttail that had been flapping in the wind at every jump Black Highwayman made during the long, wild ride.

His face became serious. His other hand grasped for the shirttail. Anxiously he ran his fingers over the seams. He looked down. There was no knot. There was no quarter. Only a cluster of wrinkles where the knot had once been. The horrible truth came to him. His twenty-five-cent piece was gone. Black Highwayman's jumps had not relieved him of Nat Love, but they had relieved Nat Love of the quarter he needed so much. Nat made up his mind that in the future he would take better care of what money he might get.

2

Double Luck

"I'M GOING TO RAFFLE HIM OFF tomorrow," said Mr. Johnson.

"How much for a chance?" one of the men asked.

"Fifty cents."

That wasn't much money to Mr. Johnson. He owned the store and the lumber yard. But fifty cents! Nat rolled the words over in his mind. That was real money. How could he get his hands on fifty cents?

The horse Mr. Johnson planned to raffle was a beautiful creature. Nat's eyes were dazzled by the burnished bay coat that the sun sparkled into bright golden-brown flashes of fire. How could he earn fifty cents? It never occurred to him that he might not hold the winning number once he had a raffle ticket.

Nat wondered how he could get half a dollar. As he approached his home he saw the chickens scratching in the barnyard. He had raised the chickens for the table and had thought of them as food for the family. He had watched after them carefully and possessed a fine flock.

His pace quickened. He approached his mother eagerly. "Can I have a couple of chickens?" he asked.

"Why, you raised them. I don't see why not," she replied.

"I mean for my own. To do what I want with them."

"You mean you don't want me to cook them?"

"No. For myself."

Breathlessly he told his mother his plan. He wanted to exchange the chickens for a raffle ticket.

When his mother heard the story she smiled. "Of course we can spare them. You raised a good flock of chickens this year. You take 'em. I never saw nobody win at a raffle, but I guess it won't do no harm. Be sure you take roosters though. Hens will lay eggs for us."

The next day Nat appeared at the drawing with the roosters. A big crowd had gathered, for a great many people had seen and admired that handsome bay horse. Like Nat, they thought the neat white blaze in the animal's face and the slender white-stockinged feet were beautiful indeed.

"Mr. Johnson," said Nat, "what are these roosters worth to you?

"Why, ah—" Mr. Johnson liked to think about only one thing at a time, and now he was concentrating on the raffle.

"Are they worth fifty cents?" Nat asked anxiously.

"Why yes, I guess so," Mr. Johnson said.

"All right. Just give me a fifty-cent raffle ticket," the boy said quickly.

Mr. Johnson's face brightened. "Here you are," he said, and handed a lottery ticket to the eager young man.

The crowd was getting impatient. "All right. I'll draw the lucky ticket," said Mr. Johnson. He reached into the box that held the stubs. Nat felt no sense of thrill, no excitement. He didn't think for a moment that he might not win.

Mr. Johnson held the ticket up for all to see. "The winning ticket is number 112," he announced.

A small mutter of disappointment ran through the crowd as everyone looked once more at his ticket to make sure he had not forgotten the numbers.

Nat lifted his own ticket. The realization that he had really won struck him like an electric shock.

"I got it! I got it!" he cried.

The low murmur of the crowd became a rising babble of relief and excitement. Nat was well liked. Everyone knew he could certainly use the bonanza. While each person had wanted to win, most everyone was pleased that the lucky winner was Nat Love.

A quick thought passed into Mr. Johnson's mind. A poor

Negro boy like Nat would have no real use for such a fancy horse. He might much better use money. "Tell you what, Nat. I'll give you fifty dollars for your horse."

"Fifty dollars?" Nat had never considered he might have so much money.

"Yes. Then I'll raffle him again." It was a statement that aroused new interest in the group. Nat was not long in making up his mind. "It's a deal," he said. "I'll take the first chance on the new raffle." He happily received the first ticket from Mr. Johnson.

Eagerly the people reached for new raffle tickets. Coins jingled and paper rustled from one hand to another. In a few minutes the solemn moment of the second drawing came. Mr. Johnson reached deep into the box, stirring the stubs to make it clear that everything was fair.

At length he drew the lucky number and held it up so all could see. Then he read out the winning number. Nat looked again at his own card. He couldn't believe what he saw. He searched for his voice which seemed to be lost from him. When he found it and was able to form words, he said, "It's mine! I got it! It's mine!"

The place was in an uproar and its center was Nat. Congratulations fell on his ear as fast as friendly slaps fell on his back. No one had ever seen such luck before.

Nat was so surprised he kept muttering, "It's mine!" more as a question than as a fact. It seemed impossible that he could hold the lucky card a second time. But it was true. Luck had come to him with a rush that day, as though to make up for the weary years it had passed him by.

3

Nat Becomes a Cowboy

NAT DIDN'T WALK on the hard country road that afternoon. He didn't even walk on air. He floated home—or at least so it seemed to him.

After he had won the horse a second time he had quickly accepted another offer of fifty dollars for the bright bay animal. And now he had a hundred dollars clutched firmly in his hand and his hand was in his pocket. Nat was taking no chances in losing his new wealth.

He quickly explained his good fortune to his mother as the children gathered near, their eyes sparkling.

"And now, this is what I want to do." Nat paused as he

searched for words. "I want to go away."

"Away?" His mother's voice contained the hollow sound of doom.

"Yes," he said calmly. "I've had all the luck I'm likely to have here. All this money has been given to me for a purpose. I want to go where I can get a good job and earn a real living."

His mother was quiet, listening.

"Lots of men are going west," he continued.

"You're not a man yet, Nathan. You're a boy," his mother said. She always called him Nathan in serious moments.

"I'm old enough to act like a man and go and find me a job," he said.

"I can't argue with that," his mother replied. "You have been the man in this house for a good spell now."

"Here. You take half." He counted out fifty dollars. "That will keep you and the kids for a long time. Maybe Jordan can help a little. I'll buy me some clothes and use the rest to get me where I must go."

"Where are you goin', son?"

"West," he said. "West, where a lot of men are goin'. It's where I'll be most likely to find a chance and a change."

It was February 10, 1869. For the first time in his life, Nat had new clothes bought at a store. Pants, a shirt, and a coat with pockets with no holes, no patches. And he had new socks, and new shoes, and a new hat, and underwear and even an extra shirt and socks. He had never possessed such things before.

After the good-byes, the promises, and the fond embraces, Nat Love turned his face westward and marched down the road. Some coins jingled in his pocket in a most friendly fashion, making a sound that was easy to walk to. The bills that remained were firmly pinned in a secret place his mother had made on an inside seam of his new pants.

In the days of snow and sun and rain and wind that followed, in fine weather and in bad, he walked west, or rode sometimes with a friendly traveler or a farmer who might stop to give him a lift. Sometimes he was able to hitch a ride on a train.

There came a day when he reached Dodge City. City? It was no more than a town, but a busy town. Fancy mustangs pranced through the streets; working horses, heads drooped low, stood tied to the hitching rails. Men moved about—businessmen, cattlemen, cowboys in fancy clothes and cowboys in work clothes.

A lot of things were going on in Dodge City, the "cowboy capital." There ought to be something for Nat to do, some place for him to fit in. Dodge City had been his goal. Now that he was here, what would he do? He didn't know anyone, so he stopped a man on the street.

"You a puncher?" the man inquired.

"Yes," Nat said. It wasn't a lie. Not really. A cowpuncher was a man who could ride a horse, and Nat could do that. He wasn't quite sure what else a cowboy did, but he could learn.

"There's an outfit from Texas about a mile out of town. You might get a job there," the man said.

"Which way?" Nat asked.

"Out that way." The man aimed a thumb over his shoulder.

"Thanks," said Nat, and headed west once more.

4

Good Eye

NAT FOUND THE TEXAS TRAIL CREW camped on the bank of a small stream. He didn't know what to expect. He had never faced a trail boss before.

The crew was breaking camp and as he approached, a dozen cowpunchers paused in their work. Nat noticed there were several Negroes among them. All of the men looked at him curiously. "Howdy," one of them said.

"Howdy," said Nat. It seemed that something more was expected of him. "Is the boss here?" he finally managed to ask.

"I'm the boss." A tall man stepped forward. "What can I do for you?"

37

"I'd like to have a job," said Nat.

"We can always use a good hand. Had any experience?"

Nat was tempted to say yes, but he thought better of it. "No, sir," he said. "Not yet. But I guess I got to start sometime."

"That's right. You shore do. Can you ride?"

"Oh, sure. I can ride all right."

"You think you're pretty good at straddlin' a cayuse, eh?"

"Yes. Pretty good. I think so."

"Bronco Jim will get a horse for you. We'll jest try you out." He turned to a tall, thick-chested man. "Bronco, saddle Good Eye. Let's see how this boy does."

The Negro cowpuncher, Bronco Jim, turned toward the horses that made up the *remuda*. Nat went with him. The boss and the other cowboys followed.

Nat wondered why the men stopped their work, but there wasn't much time to think of that because he started wondering about Good Eye. The mustang's eyes had no special quality of goodness about them. If anything, they seemed more mischievous than good. Good Eye appeared to be hiding a secret.

Good Eye was a sorrel with a rough coat that spoke of a rough life. Bronco Jim held the horse and Nat forked him easily. Nat had never used a saddle very much and he thought he lifted himself into it in a pretty good manner. He had no sooner found his seat than he was met with what seemed like a blow from a sledge hammer. The horse humped his back and Nat began to rise like a skyrocket. A quick reach for the saddle horn saved him from soaring off into space.

He found his seat again with a bang, only to lose it with another blast from below. The horse warped his backbone, did a pinwheel, pulled out all the stops and gave a bucking exhibition that brought shouts of joy and encouragement from the cowboys who had come to watch a greenhorn meet one of the most knowing bucking broncos in the *remuda*.

Good Eye sunfished, high-dived, jackknifed, chinned the moon, and just plain bucked, but however he jumped or twisted or squirmed or ran, Nat stayed on his back.

The horses in Mr. Johnson's barnyard were babies compared to Good Eye. Black Highwayman was little more than an amateur. But tough as Good Eye was, Nat Love was his master. The sorrel bronco soon found out that his burden was with him to stay.

The shouts of encouragement the cowboys had given both Good Eye and the tenderfoot now became only cheers for Nat.

He rode to the boss and dismounted. The man grabbed his hand. "That was a good show," he said. "I'm Sam Duval. This is the Duval outfit. Our brand is the Pig Pen brand."

"My name is Nat Love," Nat said.

"It takes a real good man to stay on Good Eye when he hasn't been ridden for a week and the back girth is hitched up too tight. I think I'll call you Red River Dick," said Duval. "One of the best cowpunchers I ever knew had that name. He did what you did. We all thought he was a tenderfoot, but he

rode as good as you do. He died with his boots on, and the
world needs another like him. Mind if I call you Red River
Dick?"

"No," said Nat.

"All right then. The Duval outfit will take you on. The pay
is thirty dollars a month and keep."

"That's fine," said Nat.

"But we got to change you into a cowpuncher and get you
a proper outfit. Let's go into Dodge City. We'll catch up with
the boys. They're startin' off for the Texas panhandle right
now."

It was while Nat and Sam Duval and Bronco Jim were catch-
ing up with the rest of the crew that Nat was introduced to
firearms.

Duval had completely outfitted Nat, and part of the outfit
was a Colt .45 and a Winchester rifle. Nat strapped the Colt
around his waist and thrust the Winchester in its scabbard back
of the saddle of his mount. But that was all he knew about what
to do with guns.

They were camped for dinner when Indians came on them
with a rush. The air was filled with the thunder of horses' hoofs,
the yells of the braves, the crack of guns, and the whine of
bullets.

A pack horse fell. Duval, Nat, and Bronco Jim crouched
behind it. There was no other cover for them.

Duval and Bronco began shooting. "Get that Winchester goin'," Duval shouted to Nat.

"I don't know how," Nat confessed.

"Here. Let me show you." Sam Duval gave the boy the quickest lesson in shooting anyone ever had, and Nat joined in the defense, although he said later he didn't think the Indians had anything to fear from him that day.

The rest of the Duval outfit was camped over the ridge. They had heard the noise and came to the rescue. Nat decided there and then that he would practice faithfully with both weapons. As long as guns were part of his job, he would learn that part just as well as the rest of it.

5

On the Range

IN 1872 NAT STARTED TO WORK for Pete Gallinger on the Gila River in southern Arizona. His three years with the Duval outfit had been well spent. He made several trips to Mexico to buy cattle. He learned to speak Spanish and was the outfit's chief brand reader. The latter was an important job. He had to know the brands of all the outfits on the range. Nat went to all the big roundups, looking after his employer's interests, sometimes riding eighty miles a day for days at a time.

Roundups, trail driving, range riding, and the daily work of a cowboy put Nat in constant conflict with Indians, renegades, and rustlers. It was absolutely necessary for a cowboy to understand his gun and to know how to put lead where it would do the most good. Nat had become an expert with his .45 and his rifle. Life often depended on a cowboy's skill with guns, and Nat Love's practice had paid off. He was a crack shot.

During the roundups interest always centered on a single steer, the wildest of the big longhorns on the range, the steer that could not be managed. The cowboy who could rope and ride him would get the animal as a reward, to sell as his own.

It was no easy task. The steer selected for the honor was a dangerous creature, wild, strong, with dagger-sharp horns and steel-hard hoofs. Often the cowboy who tried to ride him was rewarded with death instead of the steer.

Once, in such a contest, when his horse fell, Nat's leg was caught under the saddle, holding him fast. The steer was only a few feet away and charging. Nat, lying on the ground, drew his gun and fired. The steer stumbled and fell dead a few short inches from the struggling horse and man. You couldn't argue with a rampaging, angry steer. You saved your own skin.

Riding a mean steer was done more for sport than for the reward. It took skill of a high order to get astride a longhorn, and stay there as he jumped and pitched sideways, backward, forward, up and down, moving over the prairie like a jagged streak of lightning. But, as a cowboy's work was dangerous, so was his recreation.

Sport as well as the need for meat led the cowboys to buffalo. The excitement was not in shooting one of the animals from a distance but in roping it and securing the meat with no more than a knife or a revolver.

On one hunt Nat was attracted by a large buffalo bull. "That critter is mine," he shouted.

"You can have him," said Pete Gallinger who was riding with him. "He's a big one. I wouldn't want to tackle him myself."

Nat put his spurs to his horse and went for the bull. The well-trained cow pony soon cut the bull from the herd and during a mad race across the prairie Nat's rope settled squarely on the big buffalo's horns.

The cow pony braced himself. The slack snapped out of the rope and it became as tight as a fiddle string. Too tight. It was the horse instead of the buffalo that spilled over into the dirt. The girth broke and the saddle went tumbling over the prairie, tied to the bull's horns by the lariat, while Nat, who had soared through the air, landed with a dull thud.

"Are you all right, Nat?" asked Pete anxiously as he sprang from his horse and came running to the fallen man.

Nat sat up slowly, trying to shake away the stars that seemed to flood through his brain. "I just broke a record," he said.

"What do you mean, a record?" asked Pete.

"I broke the record for landing on the hardest spot in the West," said Nat as he began to get to his feet.

"Be glad you didn't break your neck," said Pete. "Let's shoot the buffalo so we can get your gear and go home. Here. Take my rifle."

"Not me," said Nat. "That ain't the way I play. I started out to get that buffalo the hard way, and that's the way I'm goin' to get him. I'll run that bull so far and so fast his tongue will be hangin' out like a yard of red flannel."

Nat sprang to his horse's bare back and started off, fast as a deer. The cow pony seemed to want to get even as much as Nat did, for he soon closed the distance. Running neck and neck, Nat placed the muzzle of his .45 against the buffalo's side. The shot had to be delivered exactly in the right place. A close shot was a loser's shot. "Right then," said Nat later, "I took charge of mister buffalo and my belongings."

6

Deadwood Dick

NAT TRAVELED ON ALL OF THE WESTERN TRAILS between the Gulf of Mexico and Montana. In the spring of 1876 he started on a trail drive to Dakota territory with 2,000 three-year-old longhorn steers. It was a big herd and the best cowpunchers were selected to handle them with the best horses the ranch produced.

The trail took them through New Mexico, Colorado, and Wyoming. Indians had been on the warpath and the trail crew expected trouble, but it did not come. At least it didn't come from Indians. There were only the usual storms, flooded rivers, hot days, cold nights, long hours, wind, sun, stampedes, and a brush with rustlers.

General George Armstrong Custer was on the march and the Indians were busy preparing for him. The herd was within sixty miles of the Little Big Horn basin on June 25, 1876, when Custer and the Seventh Cavalry were massacred by a horde of Indians led by Chief Sitting Bull. On July 3, the herd was delivered and on the Fourth of July, Nat and the trail crew were in the town of Deadwood to celebrate the anniversary of the signing of the Declaration of Independence.

"Did you hear there's going to be a roping contest?" said Pete Gallinger.

"No," said Nat.

"Yep, and it's for a purse of $200."

"I'm goin' to enter that contest," said Nat quickly.

"You'll be in high-class company. All the best cowboys this side of the Mississippi have come to enter it," said Bill Mitchell, one of the trail crew.

"Good. I'll have a chance to see how I rate," said Nat.

"I ain't denyin' you're the best roper I ever seen," said Pete. "But these fellers are from all over the cow country, from Montana and Dakota to the border."

Twelve cowboys entered the contest. "Well, I won the name of Red River Dick and got a job with the Duval outfit when I surprised all the boys and rode old Good Eye," Nat said.

"Yep. And I'd say you ought to be able to surprise this crowd, only—only—"

"Only what?"

"Why, gosh a'mighty, Nat, there ain't no better ropers in this country than you see right now," said Bill.

"If that's the case, us Negroes are doin' pretty good because of the twelve contestants, six are colored. But that's neither here nor there. I don't know how good these fellers are, but I do know I rode Black Highwayman when I was a squirt no more than fifteen years old. I been ridin' steers to a standstill and I been ropin' buffalo, and I can't even remember all the other critters I roped and rode."

"I don't aim to discourage you none but these fellers are the *best*."

"All right. Maybe they are the best. I aim to be the best of the best."

"Gentlemen," the umpire cried. "Your attention, please. We have here a dozen mustangs from a herd of wild horses just off the range. You can see 'em, and knowin' horseflesh, I think you will agree that these twelve critters are twelve of the wildest and most vicious horses that can be found."

"They sure look it," said Pete grimly.

"The wilder they are the better I like 'em," said Nat. He was looking not only at the horses, but at the other eleven men who were to ride in the contest. They were lean, rawboned, muscular men who had spent their lives at their work. Nat was the smallest of them all.

The umpire continued. "The horses and riders will be matched by lot. Each contestant, at the signal, must rope, throw, tie, bridle, saddle, and mount his horse in the shortest possible time. The man who does it quickest is the winner."

The twelve ropers drew lots. Nat checked his. He had drawn a big, rangy, wild-eyed roan. "That critter has got a bad eye. It seems to me he's the wildest of the lot," he said.

"You got a real outlaw there," said Pete.

"Oh, well, here we go. I've handled them before," said Nat.

The umpire raised his arm. "Ready," he warned. "Go!" His .45 cracked and twelve riders made for the excited mustangs that had been herded into one corner of the large corral.

There was a wild melee of stamping, squealing horses, twirling ropes, and shouting men. Nat had no time to watch the others. He was intent on his own business.

He took enough time to build the kind of loop he wanted. In a few moments he was ready and when his mustang was within reach, his rope snaked out and fell as he intended. The wild animal spilled on the ground. In a flash Nat was off his mount. His strong hands worked fast. He was an island of deliberate skill, of purposeful energy, of cowboy cunning in an ocean of turmoil, confusion, rash moves, and lost chances.

Each mustang was a relentless opponent. As the minutes wore on, Nat's calmness and his obvious success drew the eyes of the audience. The men who were watching knew of the pitfalls and the hazards. They knew a good workman when they saw one, and they knew they were seeing the very best. Nat held them enthralled.

Nat mounted the wild-eyed roan. The horse, with nostrils flared and flesh trembling with rage, reared but Nat stuck on his back. The signal gun cracked again. Nat had won. It took him exactly nine minutes. The time of the nearest competitor was twelve minutes and thirty seconds. It was a record and the championship of the West. And Nat Love would hold that record until the day he quit the business a decade and a half later.

The contest was over, but the mustang was not through yet. Nat Love had never forked a horse that pitched so hard. Black Highwayman, Good Eye, and the dozens of other broncos he had ridden could all take lessons from this roan. If the crowd had been awed by the work of roping, saddling, and mounting, it was aroused to a fever pitch by the exhibition of riding that Nat gave.

Yells of excitement soared into cheers of praise when the sunfishing, crow-hopping, end-swapping, and high-diving was over and the mustang decided the man on his back was the master and there to stay.

Along with the prize money, Nat got a new nickname. He was acclaimed as Deadwood Dick, champion roper of the western cattle country. Proudly, he claimed the name as well as the cash.

7

A Shooting Contest

THE ROPING CONTEST WAS OVER, but cowboy sport continued. Such a group of the best cowpunchers in the West included the most skillful marksmen with rifle and revolver, and soon a shooting contest was arranged.

"You goin' to enter the shootin' match?" asked Bill Mitchell.

Nat fingered the two .45's he wore and checked his rifle.

"Sure. Why not? I been spendin' so much money on ammunition and so much time learnin' how to be a good shot, this might be a good time to see how good I am," Nat said.

"There's high-class company in that department, too," said Pete. "There's Stormy Jim. He claims the championship."

"Championship of what?" Nat asked.

"I don't rightly know, but he claims it. And he's such a good shot that nobody is doin' much arguin' about it."

"And then there's Powder Horn Bill. He has the reputation of never missing what he shoots at," Bill declared.

"White Head is goin' to enter, too," said Pete. "He's a half-breed Indian. He generally hits what he shoots at."

"There's a good many other men here who know how to handle a rifle and a Colt," said Bill.

The umpire asked for attention. In a loud, clear voice he set forth the rules. "This here is goin' to be a shootin' contest for the rifle and the Colt .45. The rifle range will be at two distances—100 yards and 250 yards. The distance will be 150 yards for the hand gun. The bull's-eye is three inches in diameter, about the size of an apple. Each man will have fourteen shots at each range with the rifle and twelve shots with the .45."

The cowboys listened carefully. "That's fair enough," said Nat. "But I wish there would be some movin' targets."

"Sure. I never saw a man better at a movin' target than you are," said Pete. "I won't soon forget how you can plug a runnin' buffalo. Anyway, it will separate the men from the boys."

"Stormy Jim is the man to watch," said Mitchell.

The shooting went briskly. Most of it was very good.

When Stormy Jim stepped to the mark, Nat watched closely. With his .45 Jim put five of his bullets in the bull's-eye. He was

not as good with the rifle. Eight of his twenty-eight shots hit the center, although the rest were quite close.

"That's pretty good shootin'," Pete whispered. "Better than I thought."

"He's outclassed Powder Horn Bill and White Head," said Bill.

"You're up, Nat," said Pete.

Nat stepped to the mark. He lifted his Winchester to his hip.

"Gosh," said Pete. "Don't tell me Nat is goin' to shoot his rifle from the hip."

"That's exactly what he's goin' to do," said Bill. "Never saw so much confidence."

Nat not only shot from the hip, but he placed every one of his fourteen shots at each range in the charmed circle.

Then, with scarcely a pause, he handed the Winchester to Pete, drew both Colts and, shooting with both hands, put every piece of lead into the bull's-eye except two.

If Nat was the hero of Deadwood after the roping contest, he was the most popular man in the frontier town when the shooting was over.

The next day when he rode out of town with his proud and happy friends, Pete said what everyone thought. "Nat, you certainly are leaving Deadwood in a blaze of glory."

Bill Mitchell agreed. "That sure is right, Deadwood Dick," he said.

8

The Rescue

EARLY ONE AUTUMN Nat was ramrod on a drive from Arizona to Wyoming. As foreman he hired a crew of new hands and after the herd was delivered the crew broke up. They had worked their way north, and there some went west, some east, and others got jobs and remained in Wyoming. Nat began the long journey home, alone, although in the West of that day a man was never really alone. Danger was always with him.

He topped a hill as the sun nudged the jagged edge of the sky line to the west. Below him was a narrow valley, split by a stream. The slanting rays of the sun fell on railroad tracks that ran along the watercourse and stamped them with an amber stain.

A short mile down the tracks Nat saw a lonely station stand-
ing at the edge of a small cluster of deserted cattle pens and a
few shacks. He knew it was the main line of the Union Pacific
railroad, and he decided to make a call.

At the same moment he saw five horsemen at the bottom of
the hill. They had seen him and were waiting for him. He
knew that trouble was possible, but there seemed to be no way
to put off a meeting. He didn't want to turn and run and there
was no other means of avoiding them, so he continued directly
toward the waiting group.

Cautiously he touched his six-guns and glanced at the rifle in
its scabbard. It was comforting to know that his weapons were
where they should be.

As he drew close he saw the five were a tough looking bunch
of hombres.

He smiled and raised his hand in greeting. "Howdy," he said.

The men seemed friendly even though they didn't look it.

"My name's Nat Love. Headin' home for Arizona."

They greeted him with some mumbled grunts that he supposed were names, but he didn't catch them. No matter. There
were many men in the West who didn't care to be known by
their right names and Nat respected their wishes. He knew a
man wasn't supposed to ask questions. They would tell him all
they wanted him to know.

"Stoppin' over for the night?" one of them asked. This was
a violation of the code of no questions, and Nat wondered why

the strangers were interested in where he might stop.

He had thought it would be pleasant to spend the night at the station and enjoy some company for a few hours, but the question made him suspicious. He decided to play it safe. "Nope," he said easily. "I figger to ride a couple of more hours before dark. I want to make all the distance I can."

"Sure you ain't aimin' to stop?" the man insisted.

Nat was glad he had said he was going to ride on. In the West you had a right to be suspicious of a man who asked questions. "Nope. I aim to make at least six or eight miles before dark," he replied.

He saw an exchange of glances between the men. The feeling grew in him that these five ruffians were up to no good. He didn't know what it was exactly. He just felt it.

The riders jogged along, passing small talk about the weather, the price of cattle, and the looks of the country.

When they reached the station Nat raised his hand in salute. "So long," he said.

"Good ridin'."

"So long."

The words were friendly, or seemed to be, but Nat's suspicions were strong. He rode slowly past the loading pens and a freight shed.

He didn't look back until he was sure he was out of sight. Then he dismounted, checked his loaded six-guns, and started back to the lonely railroad station in the shadow of the high unpainted bars of the cattle pens.

He paused. It was deep twilight. Nat saw nothing, heard no sound. Bending low, he moved again toward the station, gliding along the side of a lonely freight car on a siding.

Though it was not dark in the open, a dim light fluttered into life in the station. Nat slid toward the faintly lit window. He peered in. In the shadowy light of a lantern he saw his five recent companions with drawn guns. They were facing a small man whose hands were raised.

"All right. Open the safe." A chill of excitement ran through Nat. The drawn Colts darkly reflected the yellow glow of the lantern.

Nat had been right in his feeling about the strangers, and now he had seen all he needed to. He didn't stop to ask questions. A man was in trouble. That was enough. But he wouldn't shoot to kill. There might be some explanation.

His weapons in his hands, Nat had kicked the door open and stood in the entrance, his guns ready for business.

"Drop your guns," he commanded, and the noise of the falling hardware echoed as it hit the floor.

Two of the five did not drop their guns, but began to turn toward the door. Nat's firearms spoke and the enemy's weapons fell. The young man at the desk had reached into a drawer before him. His hand came up holding a .45. But he moved too fast. The gun went off.

Nat, fearful for the safety of the young man, held his fire

while the five robbers rushed and crowded through a side door. When they seemed to be moving too slowly, Nat's own .45 spoke and its bullet crashed into the doorjamb.

The young man caught Nat's spirit and sank a few bullets in the floor at the feet of the frightened and scrambling thieves.

When the doorway was at last empty, Nat and the station master stepped outdoors and watched as the five men scrambled for their horses, helping speed them on by putting an occasional shot in the dirt near the excited animals. A few more shots over their heads added to the excitement as the sound of horses' hoofs faded away in the distance.

"Didn't want to kill nobody," said Nat.

"No," said the other. "No need to take 'em prisoner either. Wouldn't have no way to watch 'em proper."

The young man was E. W. Gillett who later became the General Passenger Agent of the Salt Lake road. He remained Nat's good friend throughout the years.

9

Captured by Indians

IN OCTOBER, 1876, Nat and some of the other boys started over the range hunting for strays. They scattered out to cover as much territory as possible. Nat was riding alone when the terrifying sound of Indian war whoops shattered the peacefulness of the rolling prairie.

A large party of Indians thundered out of a draw and made straight for him. They were well mounted and in full war paint. As Nat had no desire to lose his scalp he gave his horse a sharp command. The animal jumped into a dead run.

There was no help in sight so Nat headed for Yellow Horse Canyon. There he could put up the best fight possible at its narrow entrance, or he might be able to lose his pursuers in the rough, heavily wooded country in the foothills beyond.

He didn't like the idea of being chased by a lot of painted savages so he decided to throw some lead while he was on the run. Turning in his saddle from time to time to give them a shot, he had the satisfaction of seeing a brave tumble from his horse and go rolling in the dust every time his weapon spoke.

But the Indians were not idle and their bullets sang around him at a lively rate. Nat felt a heavy blow and a sharp sting in his thigh. A bullet had found its mark. But it struck no bone, and didn't amount to much. Not enough to put him out of action at any rate.

He was approaching the mouth of the canyon and had almost decided to try to escape in the woods and the rocky approach to the mountains. There were too many Indians to stand off.

Fate forced the decision. Nat felt a shock, as of a hammer blow, on his leg. A wave of searing heat followed. He didn't realize that the bullet had passed through his leg and into his horse, until half a dozen strides later when the poor creature fell headlong on the pebble-strewn floor of the canyon.

A quick movement was enough to keep his horse from falling on him. In an instant Nat scrambled behind the fallen animal and, using the dead body as a breastwork, brought his gun into action.

His aim was deadly. In his fight for life the savages suffered severe losses. Nat held them back as the minutes stretched into hours. His attackers had dismounted and scattered. Now they were slowly coming at him, protected by rocks, shooting as they closed in.

His hope was that his friends would hear the gunfire and come to his rescue. Even though their losses were great, the Indians would not leave. Without a horse Nat had no way to escape, except by a long chance when darkness came, if he could hold them off that long.

The Indians pressed hard and when his ammunition gave out, they were quick to know. At once they closed in. But Nat was no man to give up easily. Though the odds were all against him, he fought on. Severely wounded, he used his empty gun as a weapon, swinging it at each brave who came near. A circle of warriors swarmed around him. Then a crashing blow fell on his chest, and a deep black quiet swept over him.

When the darkness faded, Nat was in the Indians' camp. The wounds in his legs had been dressed with a salve made of herbs, as was another wound just over the heart that he had not realized he had. It was the one that had ended the fight. His nose and one of his fingers had nearly been cut off, too.

A tall brave stood over him. "You wake up," he said.

"Yes. I wake up," Nat agreed. The Indian spoke pretty good English, he thought, and said so.

"Yes. My father was a white man. A trapper. I am Yellow Dog."

"Why didn't you kill me?" Now that he had come through the battle with his hair still on his head, Nat was thinking of the terrible death by torture that probably would follow.

"You are brave. You are too good a man to die," said Yellow Dog. "Because you are brave, we did not kill you."

"But I gunned down a lot of your people."

"Yes," said Yellow Dog. "Bravely. Maybe you will teach our braves how to shoot so good."

"Maybe," said Nat.

The Indians kept fresh dressings on his wounds and gave him plenty of buffalo meat to eat. The first two days he was tied hand and foot, then they kept only his hands tied for two more days, and finally removed all his bonds.

Kind of foolish, Nat thought. They keep me tied tight when I wasn't able to run, and when I get better they untie me.

Three days after his capture his ears were pierced and Nat was adopted into the tribe. The holes in his ears were made with a sharp bone from a deer's leg. The Indians had no thread so a piece of deer tendon was put in the holes while they healed with the help of the herb salve. Then carved horn earrings were inserted.

It was all done with colorful ceremony and was very impressive, Nat thought. But he had no intention of becoming an Indian. He waited for his chance to escape.

He knew the Indians were keeping a close watch on him, so he entered into the affairs of the camp with enthusiasm. He

liked the dances. The war dance and the medicine dance were the most popular and, as he recovered from his wounds, he learned to perform them very well. Nat soon learned many of the ways of the Indians. He picked up enough words and sign language to carry on a conversation.

He was given the Indian name Buffalo Papoose. He discovered that he was well liked and that he was to marry the chief's daughter and receive a wedding present of a hundred ponies.

His bride-to-be was a beautiful girl, but Nat had other notions. Beautiful or not, Nat wanted to select his own wife and he had no desire to lead the life of an Indian brave.

No horse had been given to him. That would wait until he was a full-fledged brave with a squaw and a hundred ponies. But Nat had been watching the horses. He was going to need one soon, and he wanted it to be the best one. If he was going to get into a horse race, he wanted to win.

His eye finally fixed on a white and bay spotted horse. The close watch on Nat had relaxed and about thirty days from the time of his capture, his chance came.

It was a dark, cloudy night. The small hours arrived. The camp was asleep. Crawling on his hands and knees, using the greatest care, Nat moved slowly away. It was 250 yards to the place where the horses were picketed. Guards were near them. He must avoid them.

Silently he made his way. The only noise was the chirp of insects, the lonesome howl of coyotes, and, as he neared the horses, their soft, sleepy snorts.

In the darkness he found the white and bay spotted pony and slipped a skin thong through the horse's mouth. He had secured the thong some time before and carried it under his shirt, waiting for his chance to use it.

He loosened the tether and led the horse a few yards away from the others. Then, moving like a dark shadow in the moonless night, he lifted himself to his mount and turned toward his home ranch, a hundred miles away.

The spotted horse whinnied. Half a dozen horses in the Indians' *remuda* answered. Nat heard voices, questioning. They soon would find the spotted horse was gone and would try to follow him. He urged his mount on through the darkness and the dangers it held.

In the black of night, in the dimness of dawn, and the light of day, Nat rode as fast as his horse could carry him. In twelve hours he had covered the hundred miles and was safe at the ranch again.

At the time the Indians had attacked Nat his friends had been set upon by another band from the same tribe. They couldn't come to help him.

"I doubted we'd ever see you again," said Pete.

"They shot me up pretty bad and bruised me some and cut me a little. How I lived with those wounds I don't know. It's a mystery to me. They sure have some real good herb salve," said Nat.

"Where did they shoot you?" asked Pete.

"Once in the thigh, once in the leg. Then clean through my chest, over the heart, not to mention a sliced up nose and a finger that stayed on and grew again just because it couldn't stand the idea of leavin' me," replied Nat.

"How many redskins did you get, Nat?" asked Bill.

"I'm not sure," said Nat. "But this I know. It's a terrible thing to kill a man, no matter what the cause. Every man who has fallen at my hands—or who ever will—was either seeking my life or died in open warfare. It was always a case of killing or being killed."

Nat's gear had been lost in the fight with the Indians—saddle, bridle, guns, everything. But a hero should not go unrewarded. The boys at the ranch insisted on buying him a complete outfit, the best that could be secured. Nat didn't need their help, but they wanted to do it.

Nat named the bay and white pony Yellow Dog Chief, and kept him until the horse died in 1881. He never worked the horse hard or rode him on the trail. Yellow Dog Chief became the pet of everyone on the home ranch. Nat only rode him for pleasure or for a race once in a while. Few horses could outrun Yellow Dog Chief.

10

The Storm

IN THE SPRING of 1877 Nat was on another trail drive to Dodge City, one of dozens he made as a cowboy. It was an uneventful trip, but it gave him an opportunity to meet his old friend, Bat Masterson, and Masterson's brother Ed.

Bat Masterson's job was keeping order in a wild cow town. One of his problems was unruly cowboys who, filled with high spirits after the long drive on the trail, tried to shoot up the town.

"It's kind of hard to draw a line sometimes, as to the difference between fun and crime, especially when every man packs a gun," Masterson told Nat.

"A fellow ought to know the difference. It ain't fun anymore when other people get hurt," said Nat.

"I know," said Masterson. "But there are lots of these fellows who don't. It's enough sometimes to get a man to feelin' that no cowpunchers are any good."

"Course that shouldn't be, because most of 'em just want a little excitement," said Nat.

"That's what I like about you, Nat. You got good judgment. You can have your fun and still not hurt nobody."

Nat's idea of fun was to lasso a cannon at old Fort Dodge. He got his rope on it, but it was too heavy to move. The guards came and after a wild chase, they caught Nat. An officer accused him. "His notion was to take the cannon to Arizona and use it to fight Indians," he declared.

"It was all in fun," said Nat. "You know I wouldn't try to take a cannon to Arizona." It looked pretty serious for a while, but Bat Masterson told the soldiers that Nat was all right and a good law-abiding citizen, so they released him.

The following spring Nat, with the other cowboys, was out hunting strays. They roped and branded the dogies they found and then moved on to search for more. On the open range there were no fences and often cattle strayed or were driven by storms for hundreds of miles. They were gathered together at big roundups and separated by their brands and driven back to their home ranges.

Nat was well over a hundred miles from the home ranch when it began to rain and the rain turned into snow and sleet. Fog closed in on him. He couldn't see fifty yards ahead. Landmarks were lost from view, but he rode on.

An old buffalo hunter, living in a sod house, gave him a bed for the night, and also breakfast. In the morning the storm seemed to be ending and the old man told Nat he was in the Palidore River valley. The Calones Flats were seventy-five miles northwest.

Nat knew the country around the Calones Flats and knew he could get back to his home ranch from there. The old man packed a lunch for him and once again Nat started off.

He rode all that day and part of the night. The rain started again. When he stopped to give his horse rest and a chance to get a few bites of grass, he put his saddle down pointing north. Like any skillful plainsman, Nat was using some old frontier wisdom to keep his direction. It was as easy to get lost on the prairie or in the mountains as it was on the sea.

That night he lay down with his Colt and his Winchester at his side. He had just dozed off when he heard the shrill scream of a panther. Nat was on his feet in an instant, his rifle in his hands.

His horse was hobbled and was struggling against the leather thongs that held his front feet. Nat's heart stopped when the noise the animal made was punctuated by a sharp snap as the hobbles broke. He heard the hammer of hoofs as they struck against the ground. The sound faded in the distance and Nat was alone, engulfed by a black, stormy night.

His first thought was to try to catch his horse. No one knew better than he that on the prairies a man without a horse is only half a man. But he realized he might not be able to find his saddle again if he didn't take it with him. If a cowboy needs a horse, he needs a saddle almost as much, so he shouldered the forty-pound saddle and bridle and started off in the stormy night, glad that he had marked the direction. "If a horse can pack me and my gear day and night, I guess I can pack my gear," he muttered.

The grub the old man had given him was gone and Nat was hungry as a hawk. He walked all of that night and the next day without food or water, except for the muddy drops he was able to lift out of the low spots on the prairie with his cupped hand. The rain stopped for a while, but the clouds continued to hang low enough to shut off any chance of seeing landmarks.

To keep direction was a test for the best of plainsmen. His load, hunger, and thirst sapped his energy. His eyes blurred and through cracked lips he began to talk to himself. "Maybe I ain't goin' to make it—what a heavy saddle—now I know what a tired horse feels like—"

He topped a small rise in the prairie. The clouds lifted for a moment and the light of the sun sneaked through, enough to open a view of the endless expanse, with no identifying mark on it, no bush, no tree, no rock, nothing except grass, nothing—

No. There was something. Over there. He shook the fog from his eyes. It was buffalo, but to him it was more. At this moment it was life.

He crouched. His saddle slid to the ground. He looked again. There was his chance. Alone, about twenty yards from the main herd was a young calf. Simple necessity cleared Nat Love's eyes and brain. The animal was about 150 yards away, he figured.

On a good day, at another time, it would have been an easy shot. His mind went back to the time he had won the shooting contest. He lifted his rifle, but in his weakened condition his hands shook so much he lowered it again. He knew he was a dead shot, and it was not an impossible distance for him. He must control himself.

He put his weapon to his shoulder again. The gun spoke, and the buffalo calf dropped in its tracks.

Nat trudged to the place where his supper lay. His jackknife gave him blood and meat. Thirst and hunger were driven away.

He cut two chunks of meat, as much as he thought he could carry along with his gear. The weather closed in again. The wind rose and the temperature dropped. Presently sleet lashed at him. He stumbled, but he got up once more and moved on.

When he stumbled again he thought it was for the last time. A dark cloud closed in on him. In the distance, he heard a voice and then more voices. They faded away as he lost consciousness.

He awakened in the cook wagon. His friends had found him.

One hand was frozen to his saddle, the other to his rifle. They thawed him out and he was safe. The skin came off his frozen hands and feet and he spent some pain-filled days in the cook wagon, but in fifteen days Nat was ready for the saddle again. But he carried some of the marks of his adventure with him that the years could not erase.

11

A Wild Horse Drive

On a bright clear september morning, Nat and twenty of the best men from the Texas and Arizona ranges started on a mustang hunt. They carried four days' rations of dried beef, crackers, potatoes, and coffee. A mess wagon with provisions for two months had left for the wild horse country four days before.

Swinging into the saddle the group fired their guns in noisy farewell and started on a dead run across the prairies. They missed the chuck wagon, but in ten days sighted a band of about seventy-five mustangs.

"A mustang is a wild critter," Pete Gallinger said.

"We got to surround them," said Nat.

"Right. Here is how we'll do it." Pete drew a circle on the ground. "We'll form a circle like this, about ten miles across. Then, we'll take places around it. One man will be two or three miles from the other. Then, slow like, we'll start ridin' for the center of the circle, narrowin' it all the time.

"Each man will have to work sideways and cover that two or three miles, takin' good care to keep the mustangs in the circle. Remember, go slow. The herd is wild and when they see you, you'll be a mile or so away. They'll run away from you and they'll run seven or eight miles until they see one of our men on the other side of the circle." Pete described the plan carefully.

"Then," he added, "they'll run back again."

"That way," said Nat, "the wild mustangs will run maybe fifty to seventy miles or so, and will be getting pretty tired, while our horses will stay fresh."

"Just keep closin' in slow an' easy," Pete said. "The wild horses will do all the running."

"And very little eatin'," Nat added.

"Speakin' of eatin', when do we eat? We ain't got no chuck wagon," said Bill Mitchell.

"We'll hunt some meat. Buffalo is all around here. We'll jerk it and carry some with us. Two of the boys can hunt meat and bring it to us, or maybe each man will get a chance to kill his own meat," said Nat.

The buffalo were killed, and the meat cut into strips and

dried in the sun. Jerked meat can support a man for a long time.

The men took their stations and formed the giant circle. Nat spotted the wild herd first. They were a mile and a half away when they saw him. As predicted, they wheeled and ran. Although he saw them at a distance several times in the days that followed, they didn't often approach him directly.

The crew worked the wild mustangs back and forth for almost thirty days. They were finally hemmed up in a canyon, so thin and tired they were easy to handle.

"I kind of hate to break 'em," Nat said. "The poor critters have been on the run for thirty days with very little to eat and almost no sleep. But we've got to rope and ride 'em now. After that we can drive 'em back to the ranch. Then they'll get some rest and enough to eat. They'll turn into good saddle horses."

On the way home, they discovered the burned shell of the chuck wagon, the remains of an Indian massacre. Signs showed that the cook and his helper had put up a good fight.

It's a rough life on the prairie, Nat thought. But it was rough in Tennessee too. I guess it's rough everywhere. A man's got to keep at it and do a job every day. A few men can catch a herd of wild mustangs easy, if they know how. It's all in learnin' an' knowin' your business. Usually if a man knows what he's doin', and if he tries hard, he can get along all right.

The next spring Nat went with a drive of a herd of horses from the home ranch in Arizona to Junction City, Kansas.

Horses on a drive move much faster than cattle and are quite as easy to stampede. They are much more difficult to control.

Everything went well for a few days. Then the storm that everyone knew would come scowled darkly from a line of low clouds in the west. It struck the camp during the second watch, a genuine, old-fashioned, Texas storm.

The herd was uneasy during the low thunder of the storm's steady approach. A hard, sharp flash of lightning roused them into action. Although it was close, the roar of the restless feet hammering against the prairie sod came before the thunder reached the camp.

The fury of wind and rain lasted all night as the men worked in an effort to keep the herd together. It was the next day before the job was over and the frightened creatures were under control.

After breakfast the tired men continued the drive. They had a river to cross near Junction City. The heavy rain of the night before had filled its banks to the top. But the men were eager to reach their goal, and Nat decided the best thing was to push on and deliver the horses to their new owners.

The cowboys, shouting and waving their hats, and pressing from the sides and rear, urged the herd into the swollen stream. Screaming and whinnying, the frightened horses slid down the wet bank into the surging water, the leaders pushed by those in the rear.

With shouts and spurs Nat sent his horse into the dark,

brown flood. The other cowboys followed. The shouting died
down. Men and horses were intent on the task of survival in
the deep water.

Nat heard a sound. It was not wholly a cry, more of a gasp.
He turned and saw Loyd Hoedin threshing wildly in the water.
The sight lasted for only a moment. Loyd and his horse completely disappeared below the surface. The current swirled and
frothy brown bubbles covered the place where horse and man
had been.

The water was broken as the two heads came through. There
was another sound, half cry for help, half a gasping cough as
the man fought for air. They sank again.

Nat's rope was coiled on the pommel. He seized it, and auto-
matically separated the coils. It was something he had done a
thousand times on a horse and on land, but never in water
where he and his mount both fought to keep their heads free
of the river's reach.

Calling on all his strength, he lifted his arm and the loop left
his hand. The coils dropped from the other and straightened
out as the wet, water-soaked rope stretched away toward the
drowning man.

Nat's aim was good and the force of the throw was enough.
The small loop splashed down within Loyd Hoedin's reach.
He grasped it and held on with one hand. With his other hand
he held the reins and gave his horse support and guidance. Nat
pulled them to the far shore.

The other trail hands had watched the scene with awe and with fear for the safety of the two men and their horses. They crowded around when Nat and Loyd moved up on to solid earth.

There weren't enough words for Loyd to express his feelings, but he found a few that served. "Thanks, Nat. I would have been a goner if it hadn't been for you," he said.

Nat took his outstretched hand. "Come on. We got to ride or the herd will get away from us," he replied.

12

Iron Horses Come West

THE YEARS PASSED and the great wild West Nat Love found so exciting began to fade. Covered wagons came. Men broke the soil with plows and planted seed.

Sod houses rose from the prairie. Fences cut across the open ranges and the homes that were built of turf were replaced with dwellings of wood and brick. Towns grew, factories were built. Steel rails stretched over the plains and wound through the mountains.

There were no more long trail drives. Trains carried the longhorns to market.

"The West is gone," said Nat. "It ain't no fun bein' a cowboy anymore. I got to find something else to do."

"We still have ponies and there's still longhorns," said Bill Mitchell.

"But it ain't the same. Anyway, fancy cattle are comin' in too. Shorthorns, Angus, and Herefords may make beef, but longhorns got to have better cowboys. Nope. I got to find something else to do," said Nat.

"Yeah. But what?"

There was a faraway look in Nat's dark eyes. "During my life so far I had no chance to get an education, except the education of the plains and the cattle business. But this is a time of change and as long as the world is changin', I got to change too."

"The cards are stacked against you. If you ain't a cowboy, you'll have to be a farm hand or something like that," said Bill with the sound of defeat in his voice.

"Oh, no," Nat answered brightly. "Not at all. Anybody can still learn."

"Learn!" Bill exploded. "Why, you're over thirty-five years old. What more are you goin' to learn?"

"I'll figure out something," said Nat.

"Sure, you got to live. You got to have a job. But you're a black man and you don't know nothin' but being a cowboy."

"I can't argue with that, Bill. But look. What's the biggest change you see out here on the prairies?"

Bill Mitchell thought for a moment. "Why, trains," he said.

"Trains, engines, iron tracks, iron horses. That's what's made the prairie different."

"Sure," said Nat easily. "So it is trains that have taken my job. If trains have done it, why, I'll get me a job on the railroad."

"You crazy?"

"Yep. Crazy like Billy Blood, Joe Turner, and E. W. Gillett. They are working for the railroads, and there are good jobs there for a black man like me."

"Sure. On a section gang, a track layin' crew, or a tunnel driver."

"Well, I guess you never heard of George Pullman and his Pullman Palace cars," Nat replied.

"You're right. Never heard of him."

"On those long trains there are Pullman cars where people can eat and sleep. Pullman Palace cars, they call 'em, and each car is in the charge of a man. And it's a first-class job. It ought to be, because those cars are for first-class passengers." Nat grinned at his joke.

"But you're a cowpuncher. How are you goin' to deal with first-class passengers?"

"I've dealt with some first-class cowpunchers—and some low-class ones, too. It can't be much different on the railroads. People are just people. Besides, I can learn."

"By golly," Bill said, "I think you really could."

"'Course I can. And I aim to be the best Pullman porter in the country," Nat said.

So, like many other men of the Old West, Nat Love turned to the railroads to fill a life made empty by them. Like many others, he found a full and happy life and new adventures with the iron horses and steel rails that took the place of the mustangs and the western trails.

Nat enjoyed his work with the railroad. It was easy to get along with people, and it was still exciting to ride across the prairies and mountains, even if it was on a train instead of a horse.

In later years he decided to write about all his adventures in a book, and in 1907 it was published. It was called *The Life and Adventures of Nat Love: Better Known in the Cattle Country as "Deadwood Dick"—By Himself*, and in it Nat described his days on the range, his exciting trail rides, the Indian fights, the friends he made, the changes brought by the coming of the railroads. They had been good days. He had lived a good life. He was satisfied. Every job he had he did well. He enjoyed life. No man can do better than that.

Nat Love was one of the builders of our nation. He was one of the millions who used his abilities and his energies fully and wholesomely. And he enjoyed it. Who can do more?

The Author

HAROLD W. FELTON, a lawyer by profession, has long been interested in American folklore, and the first of his widely acclaimed books was an anthology of legends about Paul Bunyan. Since that time he has pursued folk heroes and tall tales with enthusiasm, and his stories for young people about Pecos Bill, John Henry, Fire-Fightin' Mose, Bowleg Bill, and Sergeant O'Keefe rank him as a master yarn-spinner.

In A HORSE NAMED JUSTIN MORGAN and WILLIAM PHIPS AND THE TREASURE SHIP, Mr. Felton dealt with facts that seemed like tall tales—history that was "almost too good to be true." In researching the stories of Jim Beckwourth, Edward Rose, and Nat Love, he discovered the same sort of material—biographies more astonishing than fiction.

Born in the Midwest, this popular author lives in New York City where he devotes his leisure time to writing.

The Illustrator

DAVID HODGES, a free-lance commercial artist, was born in Brooklyn and attended Leonardo da Vinci School of Fine Arts and the Art Students League. In addition to illustrations for numerous books, he has worked for advertising agencies and was a cartoonist for the *New Yorker* and *Saturday Evening Post*.

Mr. Hodges is married and has a grown daughter. He lives in Jamaica on Long Island.